GOD'S TEN RULES

GOD'S TEN RULES

ETHEL M. NEFF

Drawings by CHARLES V. TEMPLE

PACIFIC PRESS PUBLISHING ASSOCIATION

Mountain View, California

Brookfield, Illinois   Cristobal, Canal Zone   Omaha, Nebraska

Portland, Oregon

Contents

Johnny and his mother looked at the picture of Jesus. Underneath it were the Ten Commandments carved in white marble.

God's Rules

JOHNNY and his mother had been over to see grandmother. As they walked down the street they passed the beautiful new church with colored glass windows. The sun shone on the glass and made it sparkle like gems of many colors.

"Would you like to go in and see the new church?" mother asked.

Of course Johnny wanted to see inside the church, so they walked quietly through the front door and sat down in one of the pews.

"Johnny, can you see the picture of Jesus there in the front of the church? Right under it are God's Ten Commandments carved in white marble."

"Let's go up closer," Johnny whispered. They walked softly toward the front. "What are the commandments, mother?" he asked.

"God made some very wonderful rules a long time ago," mother explained. "He wrote them with His <u>own</u> finger on two tables of stone. They are called the Ten Commandments."

"Did God write those on the wall with His finger?" wondered Johnny, pointing to the white marble slab.

"No, dear, this is a copy of the ones He wrote. You will find them in the Bible, for God wanted them to be kept where people could find them and read them. He wanted men to obey them."

"Read God's rules to me," begged Johnny.

"All right, son; when we get home I'll read them to you from the Bible."

Johnny and his mother went out of the church and walked on toward home. "Johnny, you know rules are very important," said mother. "God made the world according to certain rules or laws. A farmer has seeds to plant, but until he puts the seeds in the ground they will not grow. It is a rule of nature that seeds must be put in the ground and given water and sunshine so that they will sprout and grow. If you plant wheat seed what will come up?"

"Wheat, of course," Johnny replied.

"If you plant beans what will come up?" his mother asked again.

"Beans!"

"That is another rule of nature. Seeds always grow to be like the plants from which they came," mother went on.

"God made rules so that this world would be a happy place in which to live. God does not make us obey His rules; He allows us to decide whether we will obey or not. If we love Him we will want to obey Him. We are the happiest when we obey God's rules."

When Johnny and mother got home they sat down on the lounge together. Mother took her Bible and read the Ten Commandments from the book of Exodus, the twentieth chapter.

"I like to hear you read the commandments, mother," said Johnny as she finished reading. "Tell me some more about them."

1

Thou shalt have no other gods before Me

2

Thou shalt not make unto thee any graven image, or any likeness of anything that is in heaven above, or that is in the earth beneath, or that is in the water under the earth: thou shalt not bow down thyself to them, nor serve them: for I the Lord thy God am a jealous God, visiting the iniquity of the fathers upon the children unto the third and fourth generation of them that hate Me; and showing mercy unto thousands of them that love Me, and keep My commandments.

3

Thou shalt not take the name of the Lord thy God in vain; for the Lord will not hold him guiltless that taketh His name in vain.

4

Remember the Sabbath day, to keep it holy. Six days shalt thou labor, and do all thy work: but the seventh day is the Sabbath of the Lord thy God: in it thou shalt not do any work, thou, nor thy son, nor thy daughter, thy manservant, nor thy maidservant, nor thy cattle, nor thy stranger that is within thy gates: for in six days the Lord made heaven and earth, the sea, and all that in them is, and rested the seventh day: wherefore the Lord blessed the Sabbath day, and hallowed it.

5

Honor thy father and thy mother: that thy days may be long upon the land which the Lord thy God giveth thee.

6

Thou shalt not kill.

7

Thou shalt not commit adultery.

8

Thou shalt not steal.

9

Thou shalt not bear false witness against thy neighbor.

10

Thou shalt not covet thy neighbor's house, thou shalt not covet thy neighbor's wife, nor his manservant, nor his maidservant, nor his ox, nor his ass, nor anything that is thy neighbor's.

Exodus 20:3-17.

"All right, son," mother agreed. "God spoke the commandments from the top of a high mountain peak called Mount Sinai. Moses and the people of Israel heard the wonderful words. The people of Israel had camped at the foot of Mount Sinai on their journey from Egypt to their new home, which they called 'The Promised Land.' They had been slaves in Egypt, but now they were to be a free people.

"God told Moses, the leader, to climb to the top of Mount Sinai while the people waited below. The mountain peak was covered with clouds, and the people could not see Moses as he went up the steep path. When Moses got to the top, he heard the voice of God above the winds:

" 'I am the Lord thy God, which have brought thee out of the land of Egypt.'

"Then God gave the Ten Commandments to Moses. God wrote them on two tables of stone which Moses had brought with him. The laws were for all the people of the world. God's ten rules or commandments have lived for hundreds

and hundreds of years, and they will con-
tinue to live forever. The Ten Commandments show all people how to live together in peace and love.

"Wouldn't you like to learn God's rules,
Johnny?" mother asked.

"Oh, yes," he exclaimed; "teach them
to me now."

"Let's go and get dinner ready now
before daddy comes home; but I promise
to help you learn the first one tomorrow,"
mother replied as she and Johnny went
to the kitchen.

"Johnny, you'll have to stay outside with Spot,"
said mother, pointing to the sign on the store.

God's First Rule

JOHNNY and his mother went for a walk the next afternoon. They took Spot, their Boston bulldog, too. On their way home mother wanted to stop at the grocery store to buy some bread and lettuce and tomatoes for dinner. "Johnny, you will have to stay outside with Spot," said mother, pointing to a sign on the store.

"Why, what does it say?"

"It says no dogs or cats are allowed in the store. It is a good rule to keep animals out of stores that sell food, don't you think?"

"Yes, that is a good rule," agreed Johnny. "Mother, you were going to teach me God's first rule today," the boy remembered.

"Oh, that is right! As soon as we get home and take the clean clothes from the line, we'll talk about God's first rule," mother answered.

Johnny put the clothespins in the bag while mother folded the fresh white sheets and towels. In a little while they were able to sit down together in the breakfast nook. (Mother took her Bible and read:

" 'Thou shalt have no other gods before Me.'

"This is God's first rule," said mother, "You remember we read them yesterday."

"Yes, I do; and we saw them carved in the stone at the church," Johnny said thoughtfully.

"In this first rule God tells us about Himself. This means that God comes first. He made us, and He made the world and everything in it. Everything belongs to God. He says in the Bible: 'Every beast of the forest is Mine, and the cattle upon a thousand hills.'

"God wants us to love Him above everything, because He gave us life, water, food, sunshine, and all the trees and flowers. We should feel God close to us when we look at the sun and the moon and the twinkling stars, for we know that God made them all."

"Did God give me to daddy and you?"

"Yes, Johnny. God gave you to us. You are our child. We are to care for you, train you, and love you. We want you to love us, too."

"I do love you and daddy," piped up Johnny.

"It is the same with God. He is our Father, and He loves us. We belong to Him, so God should be first in our love and first in our thoughts," mother explained.

"I love God, too," said Johnny.

"There are many ways to tell God we love Him. Do you know how we can show our love to Him?" mother asked.

"We can pray," Johnny answered.

"Yes, God wants us to pray to Him. He hears us, too, when we pray. We can also bring gifts to God," mother added.

"But, mother, God is in heaven; how can I give Him a gift?" puzzled Johnny.

"Suppose daddy gave you a dollar to

buy whatever you wanted. You would
want to go to the store and see what you
could find, wouldn't you? You might decide to buy a play automobile that cost
one dollar. Then suddenly you think to
yourself: I'm going to give the dollar in
the collection at the church to help someone else learn about God. Johnny, that
is telling God you love Him. You would
show you thought of Him first, and would
be giving Him a gift."

"Mother, I am going to give God the
money I have in my bank. It will help
to teach some other boy about God."

"I know God will be pleased," said
mother with a smile.

"If all the people gave the money they
had in the bank, God would have a lot,"
said Johnny.

"But there are many people in this
world who love their own things more
than they love God. Some of the things
they have are like a god to them. Whatever we love more than our heavenly
Father is an idol, or false god.

"I once knew a little girl who had a treasure that was almost like a god to her. She loved it so much she wouldn't go to sleep until it was right beside her. It really didn't amount to much, but it was the most precious thing in all the world to her."

"What was it, mother?" inquired the boy eagerly.

"It was only a fluffy wool kitty. The little girl would love it and hug it tightly. One day the kitty was gone. She couldn't find it anywhere in the house. She cried and cried. She stamped her feet and shouted naughty words. Her mother couldn't seem to comfort her, and the girl wouldn't go out to play with her little friends. She sat around all day and pouted."

"I think she was naughty," spoke up Johnny.

"Yes, she was a bad girl. It was all right for her to like her kitty, but she thought more of it than anything else. When we love anything more than God, then it crowds God out of our hearts, and we become angry when we can't have what we want.

"God said, 'Thou shalt have no other gods before Me,' and He doesn't want girls or boys to love anything above Him. Boys or girls should not think so much of their skates or dolls or bicycles that they forget God who gave them all things. God wants you and me to love Him with all our hearts."

"God loves all the people in the world, doesn't He?" asked Johnny.

"Yes, but not everyone loves Him. You see, there are many people in this world who pray and bow down to other gods, Johnny. They do not love the true God who made them."

"What kind of gods do you mean, mother?"

"Perhaps tomorrow we can talk about those gods. Now it is time for you to play. I must get busy with my work," said mother, giving Johnny a big kiss.

What Are Images?

WHILE Johnny was playing on his scooter, he saw Dickie Long across the street at Ann Stephenson's home. Dickie called: "Come here, Johnny, and see what Ann has!"

Johnny looked up and down the street to be certain that no cars were coming. Then he hurried to where Dickie and Ann were sitting on the front porch with a large wooden box between them.

"What have you got there, Ann?" asked Johnny.

"You know my uncle Bob. He has been a missionary in India. Well, he just came back, and he brought me these presents."

"Yes," interrupted Dickie, "look at this toy elephant. Ann says it was carved out of wood."

"Yes," said Ann, "and see this Indian money, and here's a piece of cloth. They call it a turban; they wrap it around the head for a hat."

"What's this?" queried Johnny, taking a silver monkey
out of the big box from India.

"It looks funny for a hat," laughed Johnny.

"Look how long it is!" exclaimed Dickie, holding up the piece of cloth as high as he could reach.

"What's this?" queried Johnny, pointing to a small monkey made of silver.

"That is an image, or idol. Uncle Bob says that many people in India bow down to little idols like this."

"They do?" exclaimed both children together.

"I thought nearly everyone worshiped God, who made the world," spoke up Johnny.

"No," answered Ann, "uncle says only a few people in India believe in the true God. Most of them worship idols made of wood or stone, or metal like this one."

Johnny noticed a small hole in the back of the idol. "What is this hole for?" he asked Ann.

"Uncle Bob says that the Indian people believe that an idol must be blessed by a priest before it is a 'god.' They take a new idol to the priest, and he takes a fly or some other insect, and blesses it, and puts it in the hole. That is supposed to give life to the idol," the girl explained.

"I wonder why people believe things like that," said Dickie.

"Johnny!" called mother, "will you please go to the store for me right away?"

"Yes, mother," said Johnny, leaving his friends and running across the street to where mother was waiting.

"Here is a note for the grocer," said mother, "and you may buy some ice cream, if you wish," she added.

When Johnny returned from the store, he told his mother about Ann's idol. "And mother, Ann says the people in India really believe that their idols answer their prayers."

"Do you remember that we were going to talk about the gods people worship?" mother reminded him.

"Yes," said Johnny; "tell me about those gods now, mother."

"Well, one of God's rules is about

images, or false gods. This is the second commandment:

" 'Thou shalt not make unto thee any graven image, or any likeness of anything that is in heaven above, or that is in the earth beneath, or that is in the water under the earth: thou shalt not bow down thyself to them, nor serve them: for I the Lord thy God am a jealous God, visiting the iniquity of the fathers upon the children unto the third and fourth generation of them that hate Me; and showing mercy unto thousands of them that love Me, and keep My commandments.'

"There are many images carved out of wood or stone that look like animals. Some images are very strange, for they look like a man, an animal, and a fish all mixed up together. The idol may have the head of a man, the body of a fish, the wings of a bird, and the feet of a bear. You can imagine some of these idols are very ugly."

"Do people pray to them?" asked Johnny.

"Yes, many people do not know any better."

"But, mother, these images can't hear people pray!"

"No, Johnny, none of these gods or images made of wood or stone ever hear people or help them; but many people think their idols hear and answer."

"God hears us when we pray, doesn't He?" asked the boy.

"Yes, indeed, He does! He hears and answers our prayers, and He gives us what is best for us. Sometimes we ask God for things that He knows are not good for us, but He knows best and gives us only that which is good for us.

"The people of India who worship idols think there are two kinds — good ones and bad ones. They think that unless they give precious gifts to the bad idols they will do them harm. They think that the gifts will keep the gods from being angry with them.

"Sometimes a little girl or boy is brought as a gift to one of these strange-looking idols, and the child is left there all alone to get hungry and cold, and sometimes even to die. The mother thinks she is pleasing the god by giving it her most precious gift. But the idol cannot help the baby or the mother — it is only a piece of stone."

"Oh, mother, I don't like that kind of god!" exclaimed Johnny.

"No, dear, and I am thankful we have a God who loves us and cares for us. He does not want us to make images out of wood or stone. God asks us to love Him above everything else because He made us. Our God loves and cares for us. The Bible tells us that He loves the little sparrows that He has made, and not one of them falls to the ground without His

God sees the little sparrow fall,
It meets His tender view;
If God so loved the little birds,
I know He loves me, too.

knowing it. Did you ever hear the little song that goes like this?

"Yes, I know that song," said Johnny. "We sing it at church."

"Then, some people pray to idols that are supposed to be good, and these idols are supposed to give them the things they need. They believe that every good thing that comes to them is a gift of the good idol, so they bow down and worship the good god."

"I am glad that God gave us His rule which tells us that He does not want us to bow down to these idols," said Johnny.

"God is good. I love Him, don't you, Johnny?" asked mother.

God's Third Rule

ONE afternoon Johnny came into the kitchen where mother was peeling apples for a pie. He looked very angry and excited. "I'll never play with Dickie again," he shouted crossly, and stamped his foot. "He's mean. He broke my new airplane, and he did it on purpose. He's an old goat," Johnny went on angrily.

"Johnny," said mother gently, "come with me. Let's have a cool drink of orange juice."

So Johnny and mother sat down together on the bench by the breakfast table and drank the sweet juice. They sipped slowly, and Johnny began to feel cooler. "I feel better now. Why did I get so mad about the airplane?" he asked his mother. "I can fix it, anyway." His mother laughed, and Johnny showed a faint smile.

"Son, there is something I want to tell you. You called Dickie a bad name. You

Johnny became very angry at Dickie for breaking his air-plane. "I'll never play with you again, Dickie," he shouted.

must never call anyone by a name like that. I am going to tell you about another of God's rules. Hand me the Bible, son. I'll read His third commandment to you," said mother, opening the Bible to the chapter where the Ten Commandments are found. She read:

" 'Thou shalt not take the name of the Lord thy God in vain; for the Lord will not hold him guiltless that taketh His name in vain.' "

Johnny listened while his mother read, and when she closed the Bible she said: "Many times when boys and girls and grown people get angry, they swear. They call people bad names, and they use God's name in very bad language. That is wrong, for our heavenly Father tells us in this commandment that we must not take His name in vain. We must always use God's name with reverence and respect.

"I had an uncle who once had been a sea captain. When he came to visit us, I remember how my mother looked sad whenever uncle talked. In almost every sentence he would use swear words."

"Didn't he know any better, mother?" asked the boy.

"Yes, I'm sure in his heart he knew better. But he had gotten into the habit of using bad language, and he did it· without knowing what he was saying," mother answered.

"One time I told uncle he shouldn't swear like that, for even his parrot copied his bad words."

"What did the parrot say, mother?" Johnny asked. "Did he say real words? I never heard a parrot talk."

"Yes, Johnny; parrots really talk and say things very plainly if they are taught. You see, my uncle took his parrot with him on his sea trips, and the parrot learned to talk from the men on the ship. We liked the beautiful green and yellow bird, though, and begged uncle to bring Polly whenever his ship was in port. Most of the time the parrot would say nice things like, 'Polly wants a cracker,' or 'Hello,' but when uncle told a story about his trips, and he used swear words, the old parrot would start swearing just like uncle."

"I wish I could have heard the parrot," Johnny said quickly.

"We children thought it was funny. Of course, Polly didn't know any better; but uncle did.

"God tells us in His rules that a person who takes His name in vain is doing wrong, and He will not excuse a person for swearing and using His name in vain. We must learn to be careful of our speech and to be sure that our talk is clean and pure. Swearing is cheap and silly. The person who swears does it because he cannot think of the right words to use, so he uses swear words," mother explained as she worked on the apple pie.

"I wish I could see a parrot and hear one talk," said Johnny wistfully.

"I have a friend living up in the hills who has a parrot. Perhaps we can go to see her sometime soon. She has had the bird for about fifteen years. You will

enjoy listening to her parrot. She says
many clever things."

"Oh, mother, when are we going? It
will be fun to see the parrot. Will she
talk to me?" Johnny asked, jumping up
and down with glee.

"Yes, Johnny, the parrot will talk to
you. We will go sometime before long to
visit this friend."

"Oh, mother, I am so glad. I can hardly
wait."

"God is particular about our words, for
He says: 'Keep thy tongue from evil.'
Psalm 34:13. It is right to use the name
of God in our prayers and in songs of
worship. When something wonderful hap-
pens to us, we should say, 'Thank you,
God.'"

"Mother, I will be careful of my words.
I am going to tell Dickie I am sorry I
was mean." And, before mother knew it,
Johnny skipped out the door to find his
playmate.

"Remember the Sabbath"

THE church bell was ringing. Nine o'clock, it tolled. Johnny liked to dress up in his best suit. He was ready to go to church, for today was the Sabbath.

Soon mother and daddy, Don, Alice, and Ted were ready to go. So they left home and walked toward the church several blocks away. On the corner Johnny met a playmate, Joan Hutchinson. "Where are you going?" Joan questioned.

"We are going to church," Johnny chirped happily.

"We don't go to church today; we go tomorrow!" Joan answered saucily.

"Tomorrow is Sunday!" Johnny promptly informed her.

"I know it. That's the day to go to church," she replied, and skipped off down the street.

Johnny was puzzled. He had never really thought about it before, but Joan

Johnny and daddy sat down near the rippling water
and watched the birds.

and her parents did go to church on Sunday. "Daddy, why do we go to church today instead of Sunday?" asked Johnny, as they walked along the sidewalk.

"Well, son, the Bible says: 'Remember the Sabbath day, to keep it holy. Six days shalt thou labor, and do all thy work: but the seventh day is the Sabbath of the Lord thy God.' We go to church today because it is the seventh day, the Sabbath. It is one of God's commandments."

"Oh, yes, mother is teaching me the Ten Commandments. She read them all to me," said Johnny quickly, remembering their talks about rules. "Mother, will you read the commandments to me again today?" She smiled and nodded in reply.

Johnny found his class at Sabbath school, and sat down quietly. He was happy. His hair was well combed, and his clean face shone.

First the leader had the children sing several songs. Johnny sang with a strong voice, for he loved music. Then everyone knelt down, and his teacher prayed to

God. She asked the heavenly Father to
care for the boys and girls and help them
to be good.

After Sabbath school Johnny found
mother and daddy. The family sat together in their usual place and listened to
the sermon. When the service was over,
they went home and had their lunch.
Then Johnny and his little dog, Spot, went
out in the back garden. The boy lay down
on the soft grass and looked up at the
sky. There were fleecy clouds in the blue
sky, and the day was warm and lovely.

While he was lying on the grass he saw
two bluebirds flying back and forth to
the apple tree. Each bird carried a straw
or string in its beak as it flew to the tree.

Johnny kept quiet and watched. He
soon spied the branch where the bluebirds
were working. His feathered friends were
building a nest. It was such fun to watch!

After a while he saw mother and daddy
walking in the yard among the flowers.
He called softly to them, for he didn't
want to disturb the birds. They came

over, and mother sat on the seat near her son. "Isn't this a lovely Sabbath day!" she exclaimed.

"Oh, yes, mother. I've been watching the bluebirds building their nest. Do you want to see them?" He showed mother and daddy the spot in the apple tree where the birds were working. They watched until the birds flew away.

"Let's go for a walk, Johnny, and see how many kinds of birds we can find," suggested daddy.

In a little while mother, daddy, and Johnny were walking through the field on their way to the creek. They sat down on the rocks near the rippling water and watched for birds. They counted many different kinds. There were sparrows, blue jays, hawks, blackbirds, robins, and the tiniest bird of all, the hummingbird. The little red-throated hummingbird captured their interest. Its wings were whirring as the bird sipped nectar from the wild flowers.

"Johnny, will you repeat the command-

ments you have been learning?" asked
daddy.

"Yes, sir, I know the first three."

"That's good. I would like to hear you
say them."

After he repeated the three rules,
daddy suggested that he learn the fourth
commandment while they sat there by
the creek. So Johnny began to learn the
fourth, or Sabbath, commandment.

> " 'Remember the Sabbath day, to keep it
> holy. Six days shalt thou labor and do all
> thy work: but the seventh day is the Sab-
> bath of the Lord thy God: in it thou shalt
> not do any work, thou, nor thy son, nor thy
> daughter, thy manservant, nor thy maid-
> servant, nor thy cattle, nor thy stranger
> that is within thy gates: for in six days the
> Lord made heaven and earth, the sea, and
> all that in them is, and rested the seventh
> day: wherefore the Lord blessed the Sab-
> bath day, and hallowed it.' "

Johnny kept repeating the words after
his father until he knew God's fourth rule.
It is a long commandment, so he had to
work hard to learn it all.

"How can we remember the Sabbath?"

"First, we can remember the Sabbath by going to church and worshiping God there," suggested mother. "Our heavenly Father is pleased when He sees us come into His house, as we are happy to see a friend come to our house to visit."

"We remember the holy Sabbath when we go out of doors and look at the beautiful things God created — the birds, the flowers, the trees, the mountains, and the rivers," daddy added.

"I know another way," spoke up Johnny. "We can read the Bible, and we can learn the commandments, as we're doing now."

Johnny sat quietly looking at the rippling water. Then he said thoughtfully: "Is that why you clean the house and cook so many good things on Friday, so you won't have to work on Sabbath?"

"That's right," mother nodded.

"Daddy never goes to his office on the Sabbath, either. We keep the Sabbath, don't we?"

"Yes," daddy added, "and you know

the men who work for me never work
on the Sabbath, either. Some of the men
do not believe in God, but everyone who
works for me has the Sabbath day for
rest anyway. The commandment says:
'In it thou shalt not do any work, thou,
nor thy son, nor thy daughter, thy manservant, nor thy maidservant, nor thy
cattle, nor thy stranger that is within thy
gates.'

"One time," continued daddy, "when
we lived on the farm, my neighbor wanted
to borrow one of my teams of horses and
the driver on Sabbath morning. He knew
I did not have the men or the horses work
on that day, so he thought he would not
be bothering me in my work to ask for
them on a day when I did not use them.
I had to explain to him that God's rule
said the cattle and the workmen were not
to work on the Sabbath either. I told him
I would let him use them on another day
of the week.

"The man could not understand, but
he said to me: 'If that's what your God

says, you'd better obey. I'll not ask you to disobey Him.'

"Months later this neighbor came to us for help when he and his family were in trouble. He told me he knew he could trust us, for we were so careful to keep God's commandments. Finally, the man and his family decided to study the Bible with us, and they are now keeping the Sabbath, too."

"That's a wonderful story, daddy!" exclaimed Johnny.

"Well, it's time for us to start home," daddy reminded mother and Johnny.

The sun had almost set when they reached the front porch of their home. The other children were back from the afternoon meeting of the young folk. The family sat down and read from the Bible. Then they knelt in prayer as the sun sank behind the hills.

"It's been a good Sabbath," mother said. "Let's all repeat the Sabbath commandment together."

When a mother quail gives the alarm, the young birds
hurry to cover and hide until the danger is past.

Father and Mother

ANGRY screams and loud excited voices were heard next door. "I won't do it—I won't," shouted a boy at the top of his voice.

"What can be the trouble?" mother asked quickly as Don and Johnny came running in the back door.

"Oh, mother," Don answered, "they are having a terrible quarrel next door. That's Jim talking back to his mother. She wants him to stay at home and fix the fence that he broke. He says he won't do it. He wants to go swimming with the boys down at the river. He doesn't seem to love his folks, he talks so mean to them."

"I'm afraid he will be punished some day," replied mother.

"What do you mean?" queried Johnny.

"Do you remember we read in the Ten Commandments about the way children should treat their parents?"

"Yes, but I can't remember exactly what it says."

"Let's find it again," said mother, taking her Bible from the shelf. She read:

" 'Honor thy father and thy mother: that thy days may be long upon the land which the Lord thy God giveth thee.'

"This is the fifth rule, son. It is the next one you were going to learn."

"What does 'honor' mean?" questioned the boy.

"Ted, suppose you tell Johnny what 'honor' means," mother suggested to her elder son who had just entered the room.

"Well," Ted replied, "to me it means to obey and respect father and mother. It means to love them and be proud of them, to make them happy, and to protect their good name."

"That's a good answer," said mother. "Even the young birds and animals are faithful in obeying their parents. When a mother quail gives the alarm that danger is near, the young birds hide instantly. If the young birds and animals did not obey, they would be eaten by a hawk or a fox. Boys and girls should obey, too. Children who do not obey their parents usually get into trouble sooner or later."

"That reminds me of a story I heard at school today," Ted spoke up. "It was about a boy named Albert. Both of his parents were killed in an accident. He was the only child in the family, so at fifteen he was left alone with nothing but debts."

"What are debts, Ted?" questioned Johnny.

"A debt is owing money or something to another person, Johnny," explained mother.

"Albert's parents had borrowed money to buy their farm and the machinery," Ted continued. "They wanted to make a good home for the family. They planted acres of fruit trees, and it took a lot of money.

"After their death when things were being settled, the farm and all the equipment had to be sold to pay the people

that Albert's father owed. The farm did
not bring enough money to pay everyone,
so the money was divided, and each person accepted a sum as payment for the
debt. They almost forgot about the rest
of the debt, for they never expected to
get any more.

"But Albert didn't forget what his
parents owed. He decided he would pay
up each person in full as soon as he could
earn the money himself. After he finished
high school he got a job in a store as an
errand boy at first. Every week Albert
put some of his small earnings in a savings account at the bank. He spent very
little money on himself. He worked hard
and did extra jobs whenever he could. In
this way he saved his money.

"As the years went by he got better
jobs in the store. His money increased
in his savings account at the bank. The
day came when Albert called all the
people together to whom his father owed
money. This is what he said to them: 'I
have called you together to pay up my

parent's debt. I want their names to be honored and respected. I want to do what they would have done if they had lived. They borrowed money from each of you because you trusted them. I don't want you to have reason to doubt their honesty. I have worked and saved enough money to pay these debts in full today.'

"Then Albert sat down and wrote a check to each person and paid him in full."

"Albert really loved his mother and father, didn't he?" Don remarked.

"Yes," agreed mother, "that was really honoring his parents."

Just then Don and Johnny looked out the window and saw Jim leaving his home. He was going off with the boys. He was having his own way even though he disobeyed his mother.

"I think that Jim doesn't honor his mother very much," Johnny soberly remarked.

"I fear not," mother answered sadly. "When boys and girls cannot get along with their parents, it is serious. They have lost one of the best gifts that God has given them.

"In the first book of the Bible there is a story of a boy who honored and obeyed his father. God told Abraham to take his son, Isaac, to a high mountain. God told Abraham to offer his son as a sacrifice."

"What is a sacrifice?" asked Johnny.

"Long ago God told His people to bring the best lamb of the flock as a gift to Him. The people offered the lamb on an altar to God. That was a sacrifice," said Ted.

"Abraham obeyed God," mother went on. "He arose early in the morning, placed wood for a fire on the back of the mule, and took Isaac with him. They came to the mountain, and Abraham built an altar. He laid the wood on the stones. Then he told his son about God's command. Isaac was young and strong. He could have run away, but he loved God and was ready to obey his father. Abraham bound Isaac and laid him on the altar. When the father was ready to offer his son, God called to Abraham and said: 'Abraham, Abraham!'

"He said, 'Here am I.'

"God said, 'Do not lay hands on the boy; do nothing of the sort to him; for I know now that you revere God, in that you have not withheld your son, your only son, from Me.'

"Then Abraham looked about him and saw a ram caught in the brush by its horns. So Abraham took the ram and offered it as an offering in the place of his son. Isaac obeyed his father, and he loved his father's God. He was willing to obey his father even though it might mean death."

"He was brave!" exclaimed Johnny.

"Yes, I think he was. He trusted his father and loved God."

One of the boys threw a stone, and it struck the little girl on the side of her head. She fell to the ground and lay still.

"Thou Shalt Not Kill"

ONE morning daddy and Johnny drove down the street to the drugstore,to get some ointment. Mother had burned her hand while she was taking some eggs out of boiling water.

"Extra! Extra!" the newsboys were calling on the streets.

"Jump out and buy a paper, Johnny!" daddy said, as he reached in his pocket for a nickel.

Johnny came running back with the newspaper, and daddy glanced at the headlines. He read aloud: "Local man murdered." Then he noticed the picture of the man on the front page. It was a man he knew, a neighbor. "Too bad," he sighed, "I wonder how it happened?" While he read on further, Johnny listened closely.

"What does it mean to be murdered, daddy?" asked the boy, repeating the big word slowly.

"It means his life was taken; he is dead. His heart has stopped, and he will never be able to talk, or move, or do anything again. He will be buried in the earth."

"I'm sorry. One of God's rules says:

" 'Thou shalt not kill.' "

"Why did this man get killed?"

"Well, it seems someone killed him for his money," daddy answered as he turned the car into the driveway.

Of course Johnny ran to tell mother about the news of the neighbor who had been killed. Daddy helped mother bandage her hand, and then they all sat down to eat breakfast. Daddy was through eating first; he said he must hurry to the office, so he hugged Johnny, and kissed mother good-by.

As mother put on her apron to wash the breakfast dishes, she began telling Johnny a story. "One time when I was a little girl something happened that I shall never forget. Several of us children were playing in a vacant lot next to our yard. There was plenty of room, and we liked to play tag there. We were all laughing and having a good time when one of the boys tripped and fell. When he got up he picked up a stone lying near by and threw it as hard as he could at one of the other boys, and yelled: 'You old meany, I'll teach you to trip me.'

"Now the stone did not hit the boy it was aimed at, but it struck one of the small girls. It hit her on the side of her head near her left eye. She fell to the ground and lay still. When the rest of us came running up we thought she was dead.

"I ran to tell my mother that Betty was hurt badly. Before mother came out, she telephoned Betty's mother, and then she called the doctor. While we waited for the doctor to arrive, mother placed a blanket over Betty to keep her warm. The doctor said that Betty was alive, but that she must go to the hospital at once. For days all of us were very sober and sad.

"The boy who threw the stone could hardly sleep or eat. He was sorry for what he'd done. He went to the hospital hoping Betty would open her eyes and look at him so he could ask her to forgive him. After a few days the boy who threw the stone became sick himself. He was heartbroken over what he had done when he lost his temper. Betty finally got well. The boy got well, too; but he was a different boy after that. He was kind to all the smaller children, and he learned to hold his temper. He did many nice things for Betty, her parents, and the neighbors."

"I'm glad Betty and the boy got well," Johnny remarked.

"Yes, we were thankful, too, that Betty did not die. I am glad that God gave the sixth commandment to help protect people. He wants everyone to have the opportunity to live and enjoy life. One who is dead doesn't know anything. He can't enjoy anything, for he's asleep, and will never wake up again in this world.

Every one of God's rules are meant for our good and our protection. If everyone would keep God's ten rules this would be a wonderful world of love, joy, and peace."

In the toy department Johnny found a tricycle that he wanted. He looked at it while mother did her shopping.

Mother and Daddy

"WHY do you live with daddy?" Johnny asked his mother one day as they were riding to town on the bus.

"I love daddy very much," mother answered in a low voice so the other passengers would not hear them.

"Is that why you married him?"

"Yes, dear, we both knew we loved each other more than anyone else, so we got married. We wanted to have our own home and children."

"Are all mammas and papas married?" Johnny wanted to know.

"Johnny, that is a difficult question to answer right here. Let's wait until we get home where it is quiet."

Johnny and his mother had an interesting time in the big stores. Johnny especially loved the toy departments. He found a tricycle that he wanted to tell daddy about.

His mother bought something and had

it wrapped up before Johnny noticed it.
When he saw the package he asked what
it was. Mother told him it was a secret.
Johnny begged to look, but mother said:
"After supper when we have our good-
night talk I'll let you see what is in the
package."

Johnny was satisfied. Then he noticed
the escalator, and wanted to go on it. An
escalator looks like regular stairsteps, but
the steps are traveling all the time. If one
steps on at the bottom he will soon be
carried to the top. Johnny and his mother
went up on one escalator, and then they
came down on the other one that moved
in the opposite direction.

It was soon time to go home. They
met daddy at his office and rode in the
family car. "Daddy, I saw a tricycle today, exactly what I want. Won't you buy
me one?" Johnny asked.

Daddy said that he might get one for
his birthday if he were a good boy.

That evening mother sat down beside
Johnny's bed to have their good-night

talk. Johnny suddenly remembered the promise and exclaimed: "Mother you were going to show me what was in the secret package."

"So I was," answered mother, "I'll get the package."

Johnny loved to see what was in packages. Mother had told him this one was not for him, but he wondered what it could possibly be. When mother opened it, Johnny saw some tiny baby clothes — two little warm shirts, some very small stockings, and two nighties.

"Mother, whom are they for?" questioned the boy.

"Listen carefully, Johnny, and I will tell you. Do you remember you asked me if all mammas and papas were married? Well, these little clothes are for a baby who has no real papa. When the baby came the father ran off and left the mother and the baby to care for themselves. The woman has no one to give her money. I thought it would be a help if I got a few clothes for the little baby."

"I'd like to see the baby," said Johnny.

"God gave a rule for people so that they would have happy homes. His rule says:

" 'Thou shalt not commit adultery.'

"When people do not obey' God's seventh rule, they bring unhappiness to themselves and to their children. For example, this baby has no father to love and care for him, or to give him his name. You see, your last name is the same as daddy's; it is an honor for you to have his name.

"It is beautiful when a young man and a young woman who love each other get married and start a home."

"I'm glad for my home," said the boy.

"Son, when you are old enough to get married, choose a good girl, and be sure you both love each other more than anyone else in the world."

"When I get married," said Johnny with sparkling eyes, "I'll pick someone just like you, mother."

Ann's Birthday Party

ANN'S birthday party was today and Johnny was invited! He was excited as he walked across the street to Ann's house at three o'clock. Johnny knew he would have a good time, and he stood first on one foot and then on the other waiting for someone to throw open the door.

"Happy birthday, Ann!" he politely said when the girl appeared.

"Oh, thank you!" she answered gaily. "Come in."

Several other boys and girls were already there. They were standing around the dining-room table laughing heartily when Johnny joined them. They were playing with a toy monkey. When the monkey was wound up he would jump and turn somersaults all over the table. How the children laughed!

"Where did you get the monkey?" asked Johnny.

The children watched the toy monkey as it jumped and turned
somersaults all over the table.

"My uncle gave it to me for my birthday," she answered.

"My, I wish I had a monkey like that!" said one of the children.

"So do I!" Johnny added.

Ann's mother came in and asked the children to follow her. She led them to the back yard, where there was a swing, a slide, a seesaw, and a sand pile. She suggested that everyone play hide-and-seek. The children scampered away quickly. They hid in the garage, in the basement, behind the hedge, and under the bushes. Ann was "it." Soon she found everyone but Johnny. Where could he have hidden? she wondered. Ann looked everywhere she could think of. Finally, she gave up, and the children hid again.

In a little while Ann's mother served refreshments — ice cream, cookies, and fruit punch. She put the goodies on a lawn table, and the children sat down to eat. Everyone was having such a good time when Ann suddenly noticed someone was missing. "Where is Johnny?" she queried. None of the children seemed to know where he was.

"Did he go home?" asked Ann's mother.

"He was playing in the swing awhile ago," Dickie spoke up.

While the children were talking about him, Johnny was at home, hiding in his own bedroom.

"Johnny, what are you doing here?" asked mother, finding him in his room. "You are supposed to be over at Ann's party."

"I—I don't feel good," he answered weakly.

"Well, we shall put you to bed, and I'll take your temperature." However, Johnny didn't seem to have a fever; he said he just didn't feel good and didn't want to eat anything. His mother said if he were no better in the morning she would call the doctor. Ann's mother telephoned to see if Johnny had come home, and his mother explained that he did not feel well.

That night Johnny could hardly close his eyes. When he finally went to sleep he tossed restlessly, and the next morning he looked as if he were sick.

The doctor came. He listened to Johnny's heart with his stethoscope; he looked in his throat, and he took his temperature. The doctor felt Johnny's body all over, but he couldn't find a thing wrong.

Later that morning Ann knocked on the door, and asked if Johnny were better. Mother asked Johnny if he would like to see Ann, but he said he didn't feel like having visitors. Ann peeped through the door anyway, and when he saw her he burst out crying.

"Why, what is the matter, Johnny; don't you want to see Ann?" his mother asked.

"No! no!" he cried. "Oh, mother, I took Ann's monkey," he wailed.

"You did what?"

"I wanted her monkey so much that I ran home from the party with it," he explained. "Ann! here is your monkey," he called as he brought the toy out from under his pillow.

"Please forgive me!" Johnny begged. "It wasn't any fun after I got home. I felt sick."

"That's because you knew you'd done something wrong," his mother explained. "It is never fun to steal or do wrong— our consciences will tell us we did wrong. They urge us to go and make it right. Of course if we pay no attention to that little voice inside of us, it will stop speaking after a while.

"Johnny, I am very sorry that you stole the monkey, but I am so glad you gave it back to Ann and asked her forgiveness. You listened to your conscience and did the right thing about it," mother continued.

"Mother, it hurt me all night. I wanted to go and tell Ann, but I couldn't let Ann know I had stolen her monkey. Please forgive me, Ann," he begged again.

"Oh, that's all right, Johnny; I hadn't

missed the monkey, but I did miss you at my party," Ann generously told her friend.

"I'll never take anything again. It's no fun." Johnny decided.

"One of God's ten rules is about stealing. It is the eighth rule, the next one you were going to learn," mother said as she got her Bible. It says:

" 'Thou shalt not steal.' "

Johnny burst out crying. "Mother, I broke one of God's rules. Will God forgive me?"

"Yes, Johnny, if you ask God to forgive you now that you have made it right with Ann."

Ann, Johnny, and his mother knelt by Johnny's bed. The boy asked God to forgive him. He decided that God's rules are good and that he would keep every one. He was learning that happiness comes from doing right.

A little squirrel peered over the side of Johnny's basket,
and then two paws took a nut and put it in his cheek.

A Trip to the Woods

ONE morning in the fall daddy and Johnny went to the cellar to look for some baskets. They were going to the woods to gather nuts, and Ann, Tommy, and Dickie were going with them.

"Oh, what fun!" Johnny thought. He loved these trips to the woods. He was particularly happy since his friends were going along.

Autumn is a beautiful time of the year to go to the woods. The paths are covered with leaves in bright colors — red, yellow, brown, and orange.

As soon as the children reached the woods where the leaves were thick on the ground, Johnny called: "Cover me up!"

Johnny lay down on a pile of leaves and the children soon had him covered except a little hole for his face. After frolicking in the leaves each one took his basket and began looking for nuts. By noon the baskets were partly filled. The

children left their baskets under the trees
where they had been picking up nuts
while they went over to a grassy spot for
a picnic lunch which Johnny's mother had
prepared for them.

Daddy and Ann sat on a log, and the
boys sat down cross-legged on the grass
while they ate the sandwiches and salad.
Everything tasted especially good in
the out-of-doors. Blue jays and gray
squirrels were waiting near by, and the
children threw bits of bread to the wild
friends. Soon a brave squirrel scampered
up and snatched the bread; then he ran
off to a near-by tree to enjoy the food.

After lunch daddy suggested that they
have a race to see who could finish filling
his basket first. Everyone rushed back to
the baskets under the trees.

"Oh, daddy," wailed Johnny, "somebody stole my nuts." He looked around
accusingly at his friends.

"Dickie did it," Tommy declared.
"Look at his basket; it's nearly full," said
the boy pointing to Dickie's basket.

"I didn't!" Dickie retorted angrily.

"Then who did?" Johnny wanted to know. "My nuts are all gone except just a few in the bottom.

"Now listen, children," spoke up daddy, "Let's not accuse each other until we know who really did do it."

"Dickie did. His basket is the fullest," accused Tommy once more.

By this time Dickie was very angry. "You're telling a lie!" he shouted.

"Come over here, all of you," commanded daddy, "Sit down under this tree. I think I know who the thief is. Be quiet; don't say a word. Everyone please watch Johnny's basket." For several minutes nobody said a word. Then they saw who had taken the nuts. A little head peered over the other side of Johnny's basket, then two paws took a nut and put it in his cheek.

"Why, the squirrel is stealing my nuts!" piped up Johnny.

They all laughed. In a few seconds the same little head appeared over the edge of Johnny's basket and took another nut.

"He's the thief!" Ann exclaimed.

"I think somebody owes Dickie an apology!" daddy said quietly. "He was falsely accused."

"I'm sorry, Dickie; please forgive me," Tommy begged.

"I'm sorry, too," Johnny added.

"I heard mother teaching you one of God's rules last night. It was on this very point," daddy continued. "Can you repeat it, son?" he asked Johnny.

"Yes, it says:

> " 'Thou shalt not bear false witness against thy neighbor.' "

"What does that mean?" Ann questioned.

"It means we are not to say untrue things about our friends," said daddy. "Tommy said Dickie stole the nuts. He was saying something untrue about Dickie. He was bearing false witness against him. Tommy is sorry, and I'm sure he will never accuse anyone again

unless he is absolutely sure. Sometimes
it may look as if someone stole, or told a
lie, but we must never say they did unless
we know it is absolutely true. A lie is
very serious—the truth is very important. A lie can cause one's friends to leave
him alone, because an untrue story hurts
other people. Let's all get busy now."

"All right," chorused the children, and
they were off to see who could get his
basket full first.

Daddy put some of his nuts in Johnny's
basket to replace those Mr. Squirrel had
taken.

Dickie finished first. "Fine work,
Dickie," daddy called. "I noticed how
quick you were at finding the nuts."

Soon everyone was through for the
day. On the way home they talked and
laughed about the little thief who had
stolen the nuts.

"I'll always be sure I'm telling the
truth about people," Tommy declared,
as he said good-by to his friends.

The green and yellow parrot looked out of the corner
of his eye at Johnny. "Name?" asked the parrot.

Parrots Can Talk

"WILL I get to see the parrot today, mother?" Johnny questioned as the family drove along in their car.

"Yes, today is the day," mother replied.

"I can hardly wait — I've never heard a parrot talk," Johnny went on.

After a while daddy turned the car up a winding road toward the hills. The countryside was beautiful in its dress of fall colors. Only the fir and pine trees were still green. The maple trees were yellow; the sumac was a brilliant red. Many shocks of corn dotted the farms, while here and there orange pumpkins and yellow squashes were piled high around.

"In a few miles we will be at the Lewises," mother remarked.

"Are they the ones who have the parrot?"

"Yes, Johnny."

Tag, the collie watchdog, met them at

the front gate, and barked his welcome.

"Hello, everybody," shouted Mr. Lewis from the door. "Welcome! we are glad to see you!"

By that time Mrs. Lewis had heard their voices, and, without taking time to remove her apron, she came out to greet her friends.

I'm making pumpkin pies," she said gaily.

After everyone had exchanged greetings, they went into the house. Mrs. Lewis took Johnny's hand, and said, "Come with me, Johnny; I've something to show you."

They went out into the kitchen. There by the stove in a box were three of the fuzziest little ducklings he had ever seen. Johnny picked up one of the fluffy balls and held it in his hands. From somewhere across the room a high voice suddenly shrieked, "Stop!"

Johnny dropped the baby duck so quickly it let out a loud "peep, peep!" It really didn't get hurt, though, for the bottom of the box was covered with straw.

"What was that?" he exclaimed.

Before Mrs. Lewis could answer, Johnny heard the squeaky voice speak again. "Ha! ha! ha! Polly wants a cracker!"

"Oh, that's Randy, the parrot," explained Mrs. Lewis.

"I never heard a parrot talk before," said Johnny, watching the parrot in his cage by the window.

The green and yellow parrot looked out of the corner of his eye at Johnny. He wanted to see what kind of boy he was, for he didn't like youngsters who teased him.

"Name?" said Randy.

"I'm Johnny," he answered. "I like you. I've wanted to see you for a long time."

"Smoke!" Randy screeched.

"Oh, my, I forgot my pies," Mrs. Lewis exclaimed as she thought of her baking. In all the excitement of her friends' coming, she had forgotten what she was doing. Fortunately, the pies were not really burned; they were only a little brown.

"Daddy, mother, come here and see Randy," Johnny called. "He talks to me."

When the rest of the family heard Johnny, they came out into the kitchen. Randy spoke out: "Name?"

"Oh, mother, listen to Randy!" Johnny was so excited he jumped up and down clapping his hands

"Stop! Stop!" screeched the parrot, flapping his wings.

"My, my," mother smiled, "won't Johnny have a treat with Randy while we are here?"

The hours fairly flew by for Johnny. He spent every moment he could sitting by the parrot's cage, and many times Alice was there, too. When it came time to go home the next day, Johnny looked sad and was about to cry.

"What's the matter, son?" daddy asked.

"I want to take Randy home with me," Johnny wailed.

"Oh, no, son; Randy has lived with the Lewises for many years. We can't take him home with us."

"I want Randy. I can't leave him."

"But the parrot is not yours. He belongs to Mrs. Lewis," said father.

Johnny was almost brokenhearted when they got in the car. "Good-by, good-by," he heard Randy screech as the car was driven off down the road.

Johnny cried and cried. "Oh, mother, I want Randy."

"But you can't have Randy. He is not ours, and you must forget about him."

Johnny acted naughty and would not listen to his father or mother; all he would say was: "I want Randy."

"Johnny, you are a bad boy, and you are also disobeying the last of God's ten rules. You haven't learned that one yet, but we shall talk about it right now."

"What does it say?" Johnny asked through his tears.

Daddy began:

"'Thou shalt not covet thy neighbor's house, thou shalt not covet thy neighbor's wife, nor his manservant, nor his maidservant, nor his ox, nor his ass, nor anything that is thy neighbor's.'"

"To covet means to want something that belongs to someone else," mother explained. "Johnny, you are coveting Randy and wishing he were yours so much that you are unhappy. You keep thinking about him until you are miserable, and that is wrong.

"There is an old story of the golden windows. A boy who had few nice things in his own home, because his parents were poor, would often stand in his own doorway at sunrise and look longingly at the big house at the top of the opposite hill. Such a wonderful house it was! Its windows were of gold, and they shone so brightly that it often made his eyes blink to look at them. 'If only our house were beautiful,' he would say. 'I would not mind wearing patched clothes and having only bread and milk for supper.'

"One afternoon his father told him he might do as he pleased, so he trudged down the hill from his house and up the other long hill. He was going to see the golden windows. But when he reached the top of the other hill he stopped in dismay. There were no golden windows, nothing but plain, common windows like his own. 'I thought you had beautiful golden windows in your house,' he said to the girl in the yard.

"'Oh, no!' she said; 'our windows aren't worth looking at, but stand beside me and you will see a lovely house with golden windows. See?' The boy looked. 'Why, that is my house,' he said, 'and I never knew we had golden windows!'"

"Did they both have golden windows?" Johnny questioned.

"Yes, they did when the sun shone on the glass windowpanes at sunrise or sunset, for it made them look like real gold. The boy had coveted, or wanted, what he thought the other one had, until he was unhappy. God wants us to be happy. We must not be miserable because we do not have the house, or car, or the parrot other people have."

"I'll try never to want anything that belongs to someone else, mother," said Johnny. "But I did have a good time with Randy."

"Love Thy Neighbor"

JOHNNY and Alice and mother were riding on the train. They were going to visit Aunt Clara. Alice was curled up in the seat reading a book that her teacher had given her, while Johnny and his mother were sitting across from Alice. The boy was already tired of traveling, so he begged: "Tell me a story, mother."

"All right. I shall tell you a story that Jesus told when He was here on earth. Jesus was talking with a group of His friends when a lawyer came up and asked a question. He wanted to know what he must do to get ready to live in heaven. Jesus asked the lawyer to tell Him what the commandment said, and the lawyer answered: 'Thou shalt love the Lord thy God with all thy heart; . . . and thy neighbor as thyself.' Then the lawyer said to Jesus: 'Who is my neighbor?' "

"Why did he ask Jesus that, mother? Our neighbors live near us."

The gray-haired lady came over and sat down by mother.
Alice and Johnny listened as she told her story.

"That is right, Johnny, as far as it goes; but Jesus said it means even more. He explained what 'our neighbor' means by telling a story. I'll read it from the Bible:

"'A certain man went down from Jerusalem to Jericho, and fell among thieves, which stripped him of his raiment, and wounded him, and departed, leaving him half dead.

"'And by chance there came down a certain priest that way: and when he saw him, he passed by on the other side.

"'And likewise a Levite, when he was at the place, came and looked on him, and passed by on the other side.

"'But a certain Samaritan, as he journeyed, came where he was: and when he saw him, he had compassion on him, and went to him, and bound up his wounds, pouring in oil and wine, and set him on his own beast, and brought him to an inn, and took care of him. And on the morrow when he departed, he took out two pence, and gave them to the host, and said unto him, Take care of him; and whatsoever thou spendest more, when I come again, I will repay thee.

" 'Which now of these three, thinkest thou, was neighbor unto him that fell among the thieves?

" 'And he said, He that showed mercy on him. Then said Jesus unto him, Go, and do thou likewise.' " Luke 10:30-37.

When mother had finished reading the story, Johnny said: "I like that Samaritan; he was a good man."

"That story surely explains how to be a good neighbor, doesn't it?" Alice said, for she had put down her book and listened, too.

"Yes, Jesus often told stories to help people understand things better."

"Being a neighbor is helping other people, isn't it?" Johnny remarked as he thought about the good Samaritan.

"And we are keeping God's commandments when we help others. Anyone who is in need is really our neighbor," mother continued.

"I am going to let Dickie use my wagon next time he wants to take it to the store to get groceries for his mother," Johnny said, catching the real meaning of "neighbor."

"You'll be a real neighbor to him, Johnny. We can show our love for God by being kind and loving to the people about us. You have been learning God's Ten Commandments. The first four rules teach us our duty to God, and the last six teach us how to live happily with our neighbors. Jesus said: 'If ye love Me, keep My commandments.' So if we obey God's ten rules we are telling our heavenly Father that we truly love Him, and we are helping to make our world a better place to live in."

Sitting across the aisle from them was a well-dressed, gray-haired lady. She had been noticing Alice and Johnny while mother was reading from the Bible. She got up and came over to their seat. "Pardon me for watching you," she said, "but I noticed you were reading the Bible."

"Please sit down," mother said pleasantly.

"I have not heard the Bible read since I was a child, many years ago, and when I saw you reading to your children it made me homesick, for I thought of my mother. She has been dead many years, but I remember how she used to read the Bible to me as you are doing. I married a man with plenty of money, but we were so busy in a gay whirl that I forgot about God and stopped going to church. We never had any children. Now he is gone, and I am a lonely old woman. My husband left me with plenty of money, so I often travel to help pass the time. I would give the world to have a family now, but when I was young I didn't want to be bothered."

"Where are you going, if I may ask?" mother said to the lady.

"I thought I would go up to the city and stay until after the Thanksgiving holidays so I wouldn't be alone in my big house when other people are having a good time with their families," she answered softly.

They visited together until it was time for mother, Johnny, and Alice to get off the train. "We would like to have you come and visit us sometime. Will you do that?"

"Oh, indeed, I would love to come!" the lady answered, with a tear in her eye. "I'll come if you will let me bring you something that I think you would like."

"Of course, but what is it you want to bring?" mother answered.

"It is something that my husband brought me from India many years ago. It is a beautiful hand-painted vase, but there is something special about it, and that is why I would like to give it to you. There is a proverb inscribed in gold characters on this vase which says: 'What is hateful to thyself do not unto thy neighbor.' You have shown yourself a true neighbor to me, a lonely old woman, and I think this vase should belong to you and your family."

"We shall be most happy to welcome you," mother answered, and she gave the lady her name and address.

"What is your name?" Alice asked before the lady had a chance to give her name to mother.

"Oh, just call me Mamie, the lonely lady," she answered.

"Too-oot, too-oot, toot, too-oot!" the train was whistling as it neared the station. The porter came to help the passengers who were getting off, and in a few minutes Johnny and Alice were in Aunt Clara's arms. Of course, the children had to tell auntie about the lonely lady they had met on the train and of how she had promised to visit them.

The days went by rapidly at auntie's farm home, for there were many things to do. There were chickens, geese, and ducks in the barnyard. Best of all, there was Shep, a shepherd dog, and Blackie, the Shetland pony.

Not long after they arrived back home, mother received a letter. It was in a handwriting that she had not seen before. "I wonder whom this can be from," mother said as she tore open the envelope. "Do you suppose it could be from the lonely lady we met on the train?"

Then mother read: "If it is convenient with you, I shall come Tuesday. I have been looking forward to this visit ever since you invited me to come." The letter was signed, "Mamie." Alice and Johnny were excited. The lonely lady would arrive tomorrow!

The next morning, mother had the bedroom clean and tidy for her guest. Alice put a bowl of yellow flowers on the table by the bed. "Mother is a good neighbor, isn't she, Alice?" Johnny said to his sister as he put a new magazine on the stand for the lady to read.

"Yes, mother always does the nicest things for people."

"Remember when she took care of baby Carol while her mother was sick in the hospital," Johnny commented.

Mother called to Alice and Johnny that

it was time to go to the depot to meet
their guest. They heard the train whistle:
"Toot, toot!"

"Here it is already!" Johnny shouted.

Mamie stepped off the train and looked
about. She smiled happily when she saw
mother, Johnny, and Alice hurrying toward her.

The lady stayed two days with them,
but she made herself so welcome that
even daddy was sorry to see her go so
soon.

The next few weeks flew by on wings.
It was the day before Christmas. No word
had come from Mamie. "I hope she will
come for Christmas," Alice wistfully said.

On Christmas Eve the family were sitting around the crackling flames of the
fireplace. They were all talking merrily,
when a knock was heard. Daddy went to
open the door. A man stood there with
a large box in his hand, and he had a
telegram addressed to mother. Mother
opened the message and read aloud:
"Sorry I can't be with you on Christmas

Day. Sending a small token of love to the family who have shown me one of God's greatest gifts, 'On earth peace, good will toward men.' "

"That's another way of saying 'love your neighbor,' isn't it?" Alice asked.

"Yes, dear, if we have the peace of God in our hearts, we shall have good will toward all men."

"God's ten rules tell us how to live that way," Johnny commented.

"Yes, indeed," daddy chimed in. "God's first four rules tell us how to have the peace of God in our hearts, and the last six how to have good will toward men."

Alice turned on the radio, and the beautiful Christmas carol, "Silent night! holy night," came from the loud speaker.

"On earth peace, good will toward men," said daddy reverently, as the family listened to the chorus.

"God's ten rules bring peace to men," said Johnny, and he began humming the carol his sister had taught him to sing.

7801